Overcoming Addictions

Companion Workbook

Dr. Frances Reid

B.O.Y. Publications, Inc.
P.O. Box 1012
Lowell, NC 28098
www.betonyourselfent.com

ISBN: 978-1-7350703-9-1

Inter and Interior Design: B.O.Y. Enterprises, Inc.

Printed in the United States.

Note to reader,

This workbook contains the assessments outlined in Overcoming Addictions: A guide
to Restoring Addiction-Damaged Relationships. To get the best use out of this
workbook, you will need to follow the instructions outlined in the book.

PRE-SCREENING ASSESSMENT *(Resource Book Page 58)*

Date of Screening/Assessment _____

Referral Source _____

PERSONAL DATA:

Name of Client: _____

Address_____

City_____ State_____ Zip Code _____

Phone # _____ DOB_____ Race _____

SSN_____

Marital Status: M   S   D

Children/Ages: _____

Relationship with Children: Check all that apply

[ ]   My children live with me

[ ]   My children live with their:

         Mother   Father   Guardian

[ ]   I don't know where my children are

[ ]   Child support: Paying   Owe   Receive

Educational Status_____

Any problems with: Reading   Writing   Math

Name of Father: _____

Address _____

Name of Mother _____

Address (if different) _____

Siblings/Ages: _____

Have you ever been abused as a child?   Yes   No

Have you ever abused anyone?   Yes   No

Are you employed?   Yes   No

What type of work can you do? _____

Last job and how long? _____

Are you available for work now?   Yes   No

Have you been, or are you currently homeless?   Yes   No

PSYCHIATRIC DATA:

Have you been hospitalized?   Yes   No

Note:_____

Are you on any medications?   Yes   No

Have you ever attempted suicide?   Yes   No

Note:_____

Have you had any suicidal thoughts in the past 6 mos?   Yes   No

Note_____

Are you currently suicidal?   Yes   No

Note:_____

Do you use drugs/alcohol?   Yes   No

Have you ever been cruel to animals?   Yes   No

Have you ever set fires?   Yes   No

SUBSTANCE USE DATA:

Primary Drug Choice _____

What age first used? _____

When is the last time used? _____

How often do you use? _____

When you first began using it what benefit did you receive from it? _____

_____

_____

What problems has it caused you? _____

_____

What does this drug do for you that you keep using in spite of the problem?

_____

_____

_____

Secondary Drug Choice _____

What age first used?_____

When is the last time used? _____

How often do you use?_____

When you first began using it what benefit did you receive from it?

_____

_____

_____

What problem has it caused you? _____

_____

What does this drug do for you that you keep using in spite of the problem?

_____

_____

Have you ever been in drug/alcohol treatment? If yes, where/when?

_____

_____

Does anyone in your family have a history of drug/alcohol use/abuse?

_____

_____

What is the longest time you have been clean from drugs/alcohol in the past ten
years? _____

What caused you to relapse? _____

_____

_____

MEDICAL DATA:

Do you have any current medical needs (treatment/medication)? _____

_____

Do you have any medical coverage? _____

Have you had a diagnosis of TB, STD, Hepatitis, HIV/AIDS? _____

If yes, when? _____

LEGAL DATA:

Do you have any criminal history? If yes, when/what? _____

_____

Does anyone in your family? _____

Have you been arrested for driving while under the influence of alcohol/drugs?

_____

Ever incarcerated? Any felony charge? _____

Are you on probation/parole? _____

Have you ever been arrested for or convicted of a weapons charge? _____

Have you ever been arrested/convicted for a sexual offense? _____

Have you assaulted anyone? _____

What are two things about yourself that you think are positive? _____

_____

_____

What are two areas you need to work on? _____

_____

Sometimes people addicted to drugs state they want treatment but in reality they are not willing to go to any length to obtain sobriety, which is what it, takes. What are you willing to do to obtain and keep sobriety?

_____

_____

_____

_____

Who will be your support system during your treatment and following treatment?_____

This Second Chance Ministry is for those truly seeking sobriety. Because of that, there is a 30-day probationary period where you will have a chance to reveal to yourself and this ministry how serious you are in obtaining a different way of life.

Is there anything you think we should know about you that I have not asked?
_____ (If so use the back)

THE WEEKLY SPIRITUAL JOURNEY
WEEK ONE

AN OVERVIEW

The individuals who participate in the Steps of Hope are addicts seeking recovery from some form of dependency. The Twelve Steps and Scriptures have been chosen as important healing tools. By consistently applying these tools to their lives, they will avail themselves to God's healing love and grace.

An innermost theme and theory of the Steps of Hope is that the healing of broken relationships is possible. To some degree or another, everyone can experience liberty from the wounds caused by broken relationships.

The Weekly Journey is designed to awaken the participants to God's grace and give them an opportunity to experience peaceful and productive living. Feelings of unworthiness, anxiety, and inferiority diminish and are replaced by spiritual strength and virtues.

Each week stresses the importance of facing oneself honestly and admitting that they have broken relationships. The Steps of Hope is a self-paced program; there are no particular time restraints. This journey is taken one step at a time, with the Twelve Steps and Scripture.

OVERVIEW QUESTIONS *(Resource Book Page 66)*

These questions are designed to assist the participant in the telling of their story

1. What personal need brings you to this second chance ministry?_____

2. Describe your practice of prayer, Bible reading, or quiet time._____

   _____

   _____

   _____

3. Describe your present spiritual condition._____

   _____

4. Recall one painful incident from childhood._____

   _____

5. What behaviors do you use to compensate for or cover your uncomfortable feelings?_____

   _____

6. How do these behaviors affect the rest of your life?_____

   _____

7. Explain how your religious experience reinforced your tendency to deny your need for healing._____

8. What unwanted behaviors do you see in your shadow?_____

   _____

   _____

PARTICIPATION AGREEMENT

The Statement *(Resource Book Page 59)*

The Participation Agreement establishes the participants' personal commitment during this week's session. Accepting the agreement is their choice. The degree of individual success, however, will depend on each person's commitment to the process and cooperation with the group.

The Participation Agreement is signed in each family group members' book during Week Four. Following is a preview of the agreement with brief explanations to clarify each statement and its value.

I agree to fully participate with my family group in working the Twelve Steps. As part of the agreement I will:

Make this group meeting a priority in my life for the designated number of weeks.

• Making the group meeting a priority means planning in advance to avoid making convenient excuses. It also means working hard to provide time and energy for all of the requirements of the step study process.

Participate fully in the group's work, discussions, activities, assignments, and projects.

• Participants' attitude must be serious concerning the work of the group and there must be a sincere commitment.

Be willing to share my experience, strength, and hope during the meeting.

- When one's story is shared with others, experiences are being heard, others learn from each others mistakes, one identifies with their own struggles, hope is shared, and a feeling and sense of community and belonging is evident.

Study the steps as thoroughly as possible by scheduling extra time for step work, reading additional materials, attending other Twelve-Step meetings, and discussing the step with more experienced members.

- One meeting is not enough to get a complete understanding of the Twelve-Step process; involvement must be consistent, and there needs to be an exposure to a variety of resources.

Maintain contact with my family group members between meetings in order to foster the fellowship, communication, and support that are developed in the meetings.

- Because of the many problems participants have already caused their biological family, it is important to establish healthy and nurturing relationships with their new family group members. Recovery cannot be experienced alone, and relationships cannot grow without consistent contact. The support groups aid participants in breaking through the denial and isolation that have affected their lives.

Support family group members by giving respectful attention, emotional support, and spiritual fellowship.

- Remember the golden rule, "Do unto others as you would have them do unto you…" Always give your undivided attention when someone is speaking, lend support for the hurting, and always be willing to give spiritual fellowship.

Be as honest as possible in all things, especially with regard to what is being learned about self, past and present.

- Denial is a common problem for many addicts; one must be intentional in their honesty. Image is not more important then honesty in the family group context.

Express true feelings about self, family group and its members, my recovery process and my relationship with God.

- Because feelings need to be expressed, family group should be a safe place for those expressions. Personal feelings and feelings that relate to other family group members can be freely expressed in this setting .

Accept any discomfort or unsettling behavior changes that may be experienced as a result of working the Twelve Steps.

- Anything worth having is worth working for. The Twelve-Step process my not be easy, but if one surrenders to God, conduct self-examinations, express themselves openly, make amends, though the process might be painful, the end results will be worth the effort.

Humbly submit to the recovery process.

- Wrongful pride and character defects can hinder ones recovery process, as well as damage family group's harmony. Humility should always be practiced. For the good and success of the family group one should humbly submit to the principles and process of the program.

Remember that God loves all and wants the best for everyone and that the ultimate goal should be to experience His will in your life.

- No program works successfully, in the end without God. Real healing begins when one surrender their will and lives to God.

Pray, meditate, and work the first three steps daily.

•   Because the Twelve-Steps are spiritual, one must be committed to maintaining contact with God through prayer and meditation.

PARTICIPATION AGREEMENT

The Commitment *(Resource Book Page 59)*

I, _____, agree to fully participate with my family group in working the Twelve Steps. As a part of my agreement, I will:

[ ] Make this family group time priority in my life for the designated number of weeks.

[ ] Participate fully in the group's work, discussions, activities, assignments, and projects.

[ ] Share my experience, strength, and hope during the meeting.

[ ] Study the steps as thoroughly as possible by scheduling extra time for step work, reading additional materials, attending other Twelve-Step meetings, and discussing the steps with more experienced members.

[ ] Maintain contact with my family group members between meetings in order to foster the fellowship, communication, and support that are developed in the meetings.

[ ] Support my family group members individually by giving them my respectful attention, emotional support, and spiritual fellowship.

[ ] Be as honest as possible in all things, especially with regard to what I am learning about myself, past and present.

[ ] Express my feelings about myself, my family group and its members, my recovery, and my relationship with God.

[ ] Accept any discomfort or unsettling behavior changes that I may experience as a result of working the Twelve Steps.

[ ] Humbly submit to the recovery process.

[ ] Remember that God loves me and wants me to succeed and that my ultimate goal is to experience God's will in my life.

[] Pray, meditate, and work the first three steps daily.

_____ _____

Signed (Participant) Date Witnessed (Family Member) Date

WEEK TWO

STARTING THE JOURNEY *(Resource Book Page 68)*

OBJECTIVES:

1. How to use biblical insight to help identify and deal with issues

2. Understand that God wants us to be restored to wholeness

3. Learn of other recourses that may be effective for mending broken relationships

QUESTIONS TO CONSIDER AS YOU START THE JOURNEY

These questions will assist participants in sharing their story

1.   Describe your past or current involvement in other Twelve-Step support or recovery groups.

_____

_____

_____

_____

2.   What do you need from a support group to feel safe?

_____

_____

_____

_____

3. What behaviors do you feel most when you participate in Steps of Hope?

_____

_____

_____

_____

HUMILITY, BROKENNESS & TRANSFORMATION

Lesson shared by Dr. John Piippo *(Resource Book Page 76)*

Humility is the foundational attitude of spiritual transformation. Pride is the enemy of all change. James 4:6 states: "God is opposed to the proud, but gives grace to the humble." You may inscribe this verse on my tombstone; it is absolutely foundational to the spiritual life.

Only a humble person can learn to grow. Pride is "the armor of darkness" says C.S. Lewis, who called pride "the great sin." It is as Lewis said, "The complete anti-God state of mind." Pride is the initial enemy of spiritual renewal and transformation.

God chooses humble people to do His work of revival, renewal and transformation. Moses, the great leader, "was a very humble man, more humble than anyone else on the face of the earth" (Numbers 12:3). One reason God chose Mary was that she viewed herself as a servant and had characteristics of submission and humility (Luke 1:18; 48). We can't preach, teach or lead anyone who is not humble. Neither can God. Nor will a proud person be "blessed," since pride's posture is not that of receiving.

To transform us God must break us of our pride. From my understanding of Scripture, personal experience, and the reading of several hundred pastor's journal, my belief is that a lot of pride yet remains in you and me. Humility is a long, deep life-lesson where much remains to be learned. Simply put, without humility transformation by God is impossible. The surgeon cannot open up and heal the patient if the patient denies they have a problem and refuses to lie down on the operating table.

Regarding spiritual transformation, what is the wisdom and counsel of God? Psalm 23 does not say, "I will pull myself up by my own bootstraps; I shall not want." Henri Nouwen says, "Maturation in a spiritual sense is a growing willingness to stretch out my arms, to have a belt put around me and to be led where I would rather not go (John 21:18)." In an era of autonomy and self-made-ness, who wants that?

Merton says that "maturity," for the Christian, is learning how to be a "sheep." As long as we remain sheep we overcome and are victorious. But as soon as we are wolves we are beaten: for then we lose the support from the Shepherd who feeds not wolves, but only sheep."

Jesus says, "Follow me, and leave your nets behind." To follow Jesus is always to leave something. Humility and brokenness require a "leaving behind." This contradicts our natural desires for success and reaching our potential by acquisition, gaining, and "upward mobility." The Bible answers in many truth-packed paradoxes.

Luke 9:24-26 To save your life. . ., lose it.

Matthew 23:12 To be lifted up and exalted . . . humble yourself

Matthew 23:11 To be considered the greatest… become a servant

Luke 22:26   If you want to rule… then be a servant

Romans 8:13 If you want to live... then you've got to die to the things of the flesh.

2 Corinthian 11:30 If you want to be strong… then boast about your weaknesses.

God's ways are different than our ways. God's process of character development and spiritual transformation involves being broken. There must come a taming of the soul. This doesn't make sense in our world's value system. As 1 Corinthian 1:18 says, "For the message of the cross is foolishness to those who are perishing, but to us who are being saved it is the power of God."

In brokenness we become less so Jesus can become more. To change, be changeable, to be transformed be transformable. Walk in pride, and God is not only unable to transform you, God is opposed to you. Learn humility, and the promise is that God's grace will be given to you.

I have been on this operating table for the past thirty-four years. The process continues. Here are some things I have learned about humility.

I have found that a humble person…

> …is not concerned to make an impression on the world.

> …sets aside the flowering of his own personality.

> …does not take himself too seriously.

> …has a sense of humor about himself.

…is not set off track by personal degradation.

…is not set off track by persona eminence.

…is not impatient when people praise or affirm him.

…is not haunted or obsessed by things said about him.

…wastes no time defending his own reputation.

…is not afraid of failure.

…is not downcast after committing a fault.

…can exist without getting any special recognition.

…is able to weigh criticism.

…doesn't believe that it sill depends on them.

…thinks of God.

…directs heart and mind to God and the things of God.

…places their confidence in the power of God.

A humble person denies the self, nails the self to the cross, and looks to Jesus.

Humility is the necessary prerequisite for spiritual transformation. It is precisely because the transformation we really need can only be affected by the Holy Spirit that pride is the great barrier to spiritual change. Like Isaiah, we need personal encounters with the Living God to see how undone and needy we are.

"But what trinkets we have sight after in life, the pursuit of what petty trifles has wasted our years as we have ministered to the enhancement of our little selves, And what needless anguishes we have suffered because our little selves were defeated, were not flattered were to cozened and petted.

But humility rests upon a holy blindness, like the blindness of him who looks steadily into the sun… the God-blinded soul sees naught of self, naught of personal degradation or of personal eminence…

Growth in humility is a measure of our growth in the habit of the God ward-directed mind. And he only is near to God who is exceedingly humble." (Thomas Kelly) "humble man is not disturbed by praise…since he is no longer concerned with himself… A man who is not humble cannot accept praise gracefully… One who has not yet learned humility becomes upset and disturbed by praise. He may even lose his patience when people praise him; he is irritated by the sense of his own unworthiness, and if he does not make a fuss about it, at least the things that have been said about him haunt him and obsess his mind. They torment him wherever he goes.

At the other extreme is the man who has no humility at all and who devours praise, if he gets any, the way a dog gobbles a chunk of meat… The humble man r4eceives praise the way a clean window takes the light of the sun. The truer and more intense the light is, the less you see of the glass.

Humility is the surest sign of strength," (Merton)

"O Christ, make me strong to overcome the desire to be wise and to be reputed wise by others as ignorant as myself. I turn from my wisdom as well as from my folly and flee to you, the wisdom of God and the power of God. Amen." (Tozer's prayer)

Renewal/Transformation Form *(Resource Book Page 79)*

THE WAY TO SALVATION

- Placing faith in Christ involves the following:
- Acknowledging our need for Christ to save us
- Turning from our will & way to God's will & way
- Accepting Christ into our hearts as Lord & Savior
- Receiving Salvation & eternal life as gifts from God
- Trusting Him to change our hearts & lives

Now you can accept Christ into your heart and receive eternal life by offering this prayer:

Lord Jesus, I confess that I am a sinner and I need your forgiveness. I thank you for dying on the cross for my sins. Today, I turn from my sins and invite you into my heart as my personal Savior. I am willing to follow and obey You as Lord of my life. Thank you for forgiving my sins and giving me eternal life. Amen

Recording Your Decision for Christ

I _____ accept Jesus Christ

Print Your full Name

as my Lord and Savior on _____.

The Date

When you accepted Jesus Christ as your Lord and Savior, the following took place:

1. Christ came into your heart & life. (Revelations 3:20)

2. Your sins were forgiven. (Colossians 1:14)

3. Your name was written in heaven. (Luke 10:20)

4. You became a child of God. (John 1:12)

5. You received a new birth. (John 1:13; 3:1-7)

6. You received eternal life. (John 5:24)

7. You received the Holy Spirit (1 John 3:24; 4:12)

The Assurance of Salvation

Your assurance of salvation is of great consequence. It is your spiritual growth and enhances your Christian witness. Your assurance must not be based on feelings, but on faith in God's word. "And this is the testimony: that God has given us eternal life, and this life is in His Son. He who has the Son has life; he who does not have the Son of God does not have life. These things have I written to you who believe in the Son of God that you may know that you have eternal life. . ." (1John 5:11-13)

A TWELVE WEEK BIBLE STUDY – WITH DAILY PRINCIPLES TO PRACTICE FOR SPIRITUAL DISCIPLINE *(Resource Book Page 80)*

Utilize this study weekly throughout the course of this program.

WEEKS ONE THROUGH TWELVE

Purpose	Problem	Procedure	Principle	Practice
Peace with God	Broken & Battered	Admit you are powerless	Romans 7:17	Submission
Peace with God	Lack of Faith	Believe God can restore	Philippians 2:13	Conversion
Peace with God	Self-Control	Give God control	Romans 12:1	Conversion
Peace with Yourself	Self-Examination	Begin self-inventory	Lamentation 3:40	Confession
Peace with Yourself	Restraint Confession	Acknowledge wrongs	James 5:16	Confession
Peace with Yourself	The lack of Transformation	Inner transformation	James 4:10	Repentance
Peace with Yourself	Defected Character	Remove shortcomings	1 John 1:9	Repentance
Peace with Others	Broken Relationships	Begin the mending process	Luke 6:31	Amends
Peace with Others	Lack Discipline	Make direct amends	Matthew 5:23-24	Amends
Peace with Others	Progress in Recovery	Continue Self Inventory	1 Corinthian 10:12	Maintenance
Keeping the Peace	Spiritual Discipline	Prayer & Meditation	Colossians 3:16	Prayer
Keeping the Peace	Lack of Ministry	Carry Message to Others	Galatians 6:1	Ministry

WEEK THREE

SUPPORT AND COMMUNITY

DISCUSSIONS TO CONSIDER: These questions continue to assist participants in sharing their story.

1.   Recall a supportive relationship you've had in the past. Describe one important aspect of that relationship experience. _____

_____

_____

_____

_____

_____

_____

_____

2.   Describe your present relationship with family members and friends.

_____

_____

_____

_____

_____

_____

_____

MUTUAL AGREEMENT

BETWEEN RECOVERY PARTNERS

The Statement *(Resource Book Page 59)*

Working with a recovery partner is extremely valuable in the addict's recovery process. The following is a list of some of the benefits along with related biblical references.

• Partners provide a non-intimidating structure of mutual accountability. For example, a partner can agree to call the other for support and prayer in abstaining from using.

"Are any among you sick? They should call for the elders of the church and have them pray over them, anointing them with oil in the name of the Lord. The prayer of faith will save the sick, and the Lord will raise them up; and anyone who has committed sins will be forgiven. Therefore confess your sins to one another, and pray for one another, so that you may be healed. The prayer of the righteous is powerful and effective." (James 5:14-16) NRSV

• Partners minister to each other's specific area of need with directed prayer each time they meet. Openly sharing thoughts and feelings helps to clarify needs in problem area. This contributes to one's freedom from the past. The focus is to live honestly in the present with realistic expectations.

"pray without ceasing," (1Thessalonians 5:17) NRSV

• Partners encourage one another to progress from a state of physical, emotional, and spiritual sickness to wholeness of life. It is normal to feel discomfort when unhealthy familiar behaviors are being transformed. Healthy behavior is a result of doing God's will.

"…And let us consider how to provoke one another to love and good deeds,." (Hebrews 10:24) NRSV

•   Partners aid one another in applying biblical truths to personal and relationship needs. When partners openly share their faults with one another, honesty, trust, and healing occur. This also means we can appropriately quote Scripture to shed light on an experience. It is not appropriate to over-spiritualize and lose the vulnerability of the moment or lose the point of what is shared.

"Then Jesus said to the Jews who had believed in him, "If you continue in my word, you are truly my disciples; and you will know the truth, and the truth will make you free." (John 8:31-32) NRSV

In establishing a relationship with a recovery partner it is important to agree on how the partners want to interact with one another, and the length of time in which the agreement will be in effect. Times can be selected to evaluate the quality of the relationship. It is helpful to have an understanding of how the relationship or agreement can be ended.

Following is a preview of the agreement with brief explanations to clarify each statement and its value.

Focus on the Twelve Steps as a tool to enhance one's relationship with God and others.

•   As times encouragement or confrontation is needed when one has stopped working the steps. I a partner am unavailable or can not answer a question, seek out other Twelve-Step fellow travelers to help in understanding how they use this discipline in their recovery. It is in appropriate to impose personal views on one's recovery partner, particularly regarding one's relationship with God.

Be available for phone calls or meeting in person.

•   A key to success in recovery is making and keeping commitments. Making a commitment to being available may be something new, but it is an important part of the process. Healing and change are easier when someone is available to offer support and encouragement.

Share true feelings between each other.

•   Rigorous honest is important when sharing feelings. Healing is supported when partners tell the truth. Feelings require acknowledgment and appropriate expression without their being judged as right or wrong. Selective disclosure when talking about feelings may create doubt between partners.

Refrain from giving lengthy explanations when sharing.

•   Sharing is not a lengthy or dramatic re-creation of personal stories. Referring to journal notes or workbook writing keeps the focus on the subject shared and helps to avoid intellectualizing.

Complete the homework assignment each week.

•   Partners can provide support and encouragement to each other in completing the assignment. Sharing the results of homework writing often helps clarify the meaning of questions and is an opportunity to hear another perspective.

Spend a minimum of 15 minutes each day reading Scripture, praying, and meditating, including prayer for your recovery partner.

• Prayer is talking to God, meditation is listening to God. Spending time in prayer and meditation can be a vital part of the recovery process. This is a spiritual program founded upon seeking to know God's will and experiencing his grace.

Respect confidentiality and refrain from gossip.

• This program I built on trust. Fear of gossip may prevent some people from honestly sharing the pain of their lies. Healing will be hindered unless there is trust tat personal matters between partners will remain confidential.

Accept discomfort as part of the healing process, and be willing to talk about it.

• Some meetings may be painful when memories of certain events or hurtful feelings are recalled. It is important to have a recovery partner available to show compassion and be supportive as we confront painful issues that cause us discomfort. It is best to admit the discomfort and deal with it. A recovery partner can help us face the issues without reverting to old coping methods.

Support one another by listening attentively and offering constructive feedback.

• Listening attentively and offering feedback enables us to explore options and possible courses of action. This can strengthen one another's ability to make healthy choices that provide good results. Feedback, however, must not be confused with unsolicited advice.

Refrain from spiritualizing or intellectualizing when sharing.

- Partners neither are not spiritual directors to each other nor are they sources of advice in areas more appropriately handled by clergy or a professional therapist. Instead, partners share their won experience, strength, and hope with one another. In spiritual matters, recovery partners share how God works in their lies without over=spiritualizing or preaching.

MUTUAL AGREEMENT

BETWEEN RECOVERY PARTNERS

The Commitment *(Resource Book Page 59)*

I, _____, agree to enter a recovery Partner agreement with

_____, as a way to be supported and held accountable in dealing with behaviors that keep me from the best God has for me. I am seeking recovery from these ineffective patterns of behavior so that I may become more fully connected to God, others, and myself.

I will make a sincere effort to:

[ ]   Focus on the Twelve Steps as a tool to enhance my relationship with God and others.

[ ]   Be available for phone calls or meetings in person.

[ ]   Share my true feelings with my recovery partner.

[ ]   Refrain from giving lengthy explanations when sharing.

[ ]   Complete the homework assignment each week.

[ ]   Spend a minimum of 15 minutes each day reading Scripture, praying and meditating, including specific prayer for my recovery partner.

[]   Accept discomfort as part of the healing process, and be willing to talk about it.

[]   Support one another by listening attentively and offering my constructive feedback.

[]   Refrain from spiritualizing or intellectualizing when sharing.

The term of this agreement is from _____ to _____.

We agree to meet _____ (weekly, monthly, etc.) outside the weekly

meetings, and spend time reviewing the progress and compatibility of this

relationship. If for any reason either partner feels this relationship does not serve

his/her recovery needs, notifying the other can end the agreement.

_____   _____

Signed   Partner

COMMON BEHAVIOR CHARACTERISTICS

WEEK FOUR

Family group participation for this week helps individuals identify some of their thoughts, feelings, and behaviors.

1.	We have feelings of low self-esteem that cause us to judge others and ourselves without mercy. We cover up or compensate by trying to be perfect, take responsibility for others, attempt to control the outcome of unpredictable events, get angry when things don't go our way, or gossip instead of confronting an issue.

A.	How do you compensate for your feelings of low self-esteem?

_____

_____

_____

2.	We tend to isolate ourselves and to feel uneasy around other people, especially authority figures.

A.	How do you isolate yourself from others?

_____

_____

_____

B.	What do you do when you are around authority figures?

_____

_____

_____

_____

3.   We are approval seekers and will do anything to make people like us. We are extremely loyal even in the face of evidence that suggests loyalty is underserved.

A.   How do you seek approval from your family or friends?

_____

_____

_____

4.   Angry people and personal criticism intimidate us. This causes us to feel anxious and overly sensitive.

A.   When is your first recollection of being intimidated by an angry person?

_____

_____

_____

B.   How do you respond to personal criticism?

_____

_____

_____

5.   We habitually choose to have relationships with emotionally unavailable people with addictive personalities. We are usually less attracted to healthy, caring people.

A.   The people in my life with addictive/compulsive personality styles are

_____

_____

_____

B.   The relationships from which I receive the most nurture and support are

_____

_____

_____

6.   We live as victims and are attracted to other victims in our love and friendship relationships. We confuse love with pity and tend to "love" people we can pity and rescue.

A.   The last time I noticed that I was "being used" by someone was when?

_____

_____

_____

B.   How do you try to rescue others?

_____

_____

_____

7.   We are either overly responsible or very irresponsible. We try to solve others' problems or expect others to be responsible for us. This enables us to avoid looking closely at our own behavior.

A.   When do you feel overly responsible?

_____

_____

_____

_____

B.   When do you feel irresponsible?

_____

_____

_____

8.   We feel guilty when we stand up for ourselves or act assertively. We give in to others instead of taking care of ourselves.

A.   When were you afraid to express your true feelings and gave into someone, explain?

_____

_____

_____

9.   We deny, minimize, or repress our feelings from our traumatic childhoods. We have difficulty expressing our feelings and are unaware of the impact this has on our lives.

A.   When have you denied, minimized, or repressed your feelings?

_____

_____

_____

_____

10.   We are dependent personalities who are terrified of rejection or abandonment. We tend to stay in jobs or relationships that are harmful to us. Our fears can either stop us from ending hurtful relationships or prevent us from entering healthy, rewarding ones.

A.   I fear rejection or abandonment the most in my relationship with

_____

_____

_____

_____

B.   I currently deal with this fear by

_____

_____

_____

11.   Denial, isolation, control, and misplaced guilt are symptoms of family dysfunction. Because of these behaviors, we feel hopeless and helpless.

A.   The results of my family's dysfunction are seen in my life when I

_____

_____

_____

12. We have difficulty with intimate relationships. We feel insecure and lack trust in others. We don't have clearly defined boundaries and become enmeshed with our partner's needs and emotions.

A.   My present difficulties with intimate relationships are

_____

_____

_____

_____

B.   Who do you have difficulty trusting and why?

_____

_____

_____

_____

13.   We have difficulty following projects through from beginning to end

A.   When I lack motivation or procrastinate, I feel

_____

_____

_____

_____

B.   The current projects I'm not completing are

_____

_____

_____

_____

14. We have a strong need to be in control. We overreact to change over which we have no control.

A.   When I am not in control I fear

_____

_____

_____

_____

B.	When I am not in control I feel

_____

_____

_____

_____

15.	We tend to be impulsive. We take action before considering alternative behaviors or possible consequences.

A.	My impulsiveness caused me to make a poor decision when I

_____

_____

_____

_____

PREPARING FOR THE COMMUNITY

These questions will begin to prepare you for the Community

1.   Which three characteristics would you like to share with others?

_____

_____

_____

_____

_____

2.   What is your overall reaction to reading the characteristics? To what degree do they apply to you?

_____

_____

_____

_____

_____

3.   In what areas do you see yourself as overly responsible or very irresponsible?

_____

_____

_____

_____

_____

4.   Which characteristic do you most closely relate to? How does this characteristic present itself in your life?

_____

_____

WEEKS FIVE – TWELVE

Over the next eight weeks Steps Five through Twelve will be studied.

STEP ONE

This step is used as an example of the remaining weekly group sessions

STEP FIVE: Admitted to God, to ourselves, and to another human being the exact nature of our wrongs.

SCRIPTURE: Therefore confess your sins to one another, and pray for one another, so that you may be healed. The prayer of the righteous is powerful and effective.

SESSION OUTLINE FOR DISCUSSION

1.   Understanding Step-Five

2.   Working Step-Five

3.   Preparing for Step-Five

4.   Prayer for Step-Five

Personal Reflection: Your growing relationship with God gives you the courage to examine yourselves, accept who you are, and reveal your true selves. Step Five helps you knowledge and discard your old survival skills and move toward a new and healthier life. Being thorough and honest in completing your inventory places you in a position to move forward.

QUESTIONS FOR DISUCSSION

1. Describe some feelings you experienced when making your inventory.

_____

_____

_____

_____

2. How did doing your inventory bring you closer to mending broken relationships

_____

_____

_____

_____

3. What area of your life is causing you the most sadness?

_____

_____

_____

_____

4. What events in your life caused you to realize the extent of your pain?

_____

_____

_____

_____

GROUP ACTIVITY

These activities were designed to help you alleviate your struggles and fill your emptiness, as you allow the power of God to fill your life. (*Resource Book Page 46*)

ACTIVITY # 1: **"In the Dark"**

Supplies Needed: Paper and pens.

Objective: To experience the powerlessness and unmanageability of trying to write or draw something in the dark.

[ ] Make preparations to draw or write something (e.g., a self-portrait, a drawing of a favorite pet, or a letter to self).

[ ] Turn off the lights so that it is completely dark and begin. Allow about five minutes. If darkness is not possible, ask people to close their eyes.

[ ] When the time is up each person shares his or her work, one at a time. To create suspense and prolong the fun, keep the work face down until it's your turn to share.

[ ] Finally, discuss how this exercise in the dark is similar to feelings of powerlessness and unmanageability.

ACTIVITY: # 2: "A Portrait of Unmanageability!"

Supplies Needed: Plain white paper, colored pencils or crayons, tables or clipboards, and imagination.

Objective: To artistically express unmanageability through drawing.

[]   Draw a picture representing the unmanageability of your life (e.g., a furnace burning up money to demonstrate financial unmanageability, or several monsters circling your head to represent your fears). Imagination and creativity are the important elements.

[]   At the end of the exercise, show and explain your picture to the group.

ACTIVITY # 3: "Prayers for Step One"

Supplies Needed: Paper and pens.

Objective: To write a Step One Prayer and share the prayer with the group

[]   Begin by writing a Step One prayer. It is helpful to recall Step One themes from the family group discussions. Study away from themes or concepts that are related to future steps. For example, write about powerlessness and unmanageability rather than faith or amends.

[]   Assume a prayerful mood while each participant reads his or her own paper. To create a soft atmosphere, lights could be turned off and each participant could be given a candle.

Source: Adapted from Recovery Opinion: The Complete Guide

ALCOHOL USE DISORDERS IDENTIFICATION TEST (Audit)

This audit was done on a group of individuals who are not considered substance abuse victims.

Directions: Answer the following questions by filling in the blank with the correct number. Choose from the following for questions 1 & 2:

Never being   (0)

Monthly or less   (1)

2 to 3 times a month   (2)

2 to 3 times a week   (3)

4 or more times a week   (4)

1. How often do you have a drink containing alcohol?

2. How many alcoholic drinks do you have on a typical drinking day?

Choose from the following for questions 3 thru 10:

        Never   (0)

        Less than monthly   (1)

        Monthly   (2)

        Weekly   (3)

3. How often do you have six or more drinks on one occasion?

4. How often during the past year have you found that you were unable to
Stop drinking once you had started?

5. How often during the past year have you failed to do what was normally expected of you because of drinking?

6. How often during the past year have you needed a drink first thing in the morning to get yourself going after a heavy drinking session?

7. How often during the past year have you had a feeling of guilt or remorse?

After drinking?

8. How often during the past year have you been unable to remember what happened while drinking?

Happened the night before because you were drinking?

9. Have you or someone else ever been injured as a result of your drinking?

10. Has a relative, friend, or doctor or other health worker been concerned about your drinking or suggested you cut down?

Record the total score. _____

Eight (8) or higher means you should get professional evaluation.

Source: World Health Organization (WHO), 1987.

The Standard for Treatment

The standard for treatment and recovery from life's dependencies is the Twelve Step program developed by the Alcohol Anonymous (AA) group. This program provides a spiritual blueprint for the addict's recovery. Participants are encouraged to come to terms with their addiction and rely on God, while they journey through the "Steps of Hope."

The foundational basis for the treatment provided for the participant is the Scripture which has been attached to the twelve steps as a support. Participants must be willing to follow the program offered by "Steps of Hope." As part of the standard for treatment and the strategy for recovery, there are three things that are key.

1.   Stay away from drugs, alcohol or substance abuse paraphernalia forever.

2.   Change your lifestyle

3.   Get help from a support group and stick with them.

A GUIDE TO RECOVERY AND HEALING

Accept Christ as Lord and Savior – It does not matter what the participant's physical condition is. The opportunity to lead the addict to Christ is never taken for granted. One should never under estimate the power of God to penetrate the mental, physical and emotional condition or state of an individual prior to salvation. The Scripture says, "Whosoever will let him come…"

The "Steps of Hope's" teachings are based on six basic assumptions. The idea is taken from the Oxford Group founded by William Griffith Wilson and Dr. Robert Holbrook Smith.

1.   All are sinners

2.   All can be changed

3.   Repentance is a prerequisite to change

4.   Repentance allows for direct access to God

5.   Miracles are still possible

6.   Once saved, share your testimony that others might be saved

In addition, this ministry teaches that one must surrender to God, follow His directions and periodically do a self-check to be sure that proper guidance is being received and followed. Restitution is practiced followed by sharing that others might be set free.

SYMPTOMS OF CHEMICAL DEPENDENCY

The following survey has helped the "Steps of Hope" gain a better understanding for alcohol, drug dependency, and mood swings.

AN ALCOHOL/DRUG SURVEY

Directions: Please answer the following questions to the best of your ability. Those symptoms that are given more to an alcoholic, place an "A" in the space. If the symptoms reflect that of drug dependency, place a "D" in the space. If the symptoms reflect both users, place a "B" in the space.

1. Identify these signs of growing preoccupation and anticipation of victims.
_____ They participate more during daytime activities.
_____ They have a growing involvement do to activities in bats, buildings or with people
_____ They participate because of a growing number of physical complaints
_____ They keep track of prescribed times for using.
_____ They participate more during vacation times.

2. They have a growing need to participate during times of stress.
_____ Emergency situations
_____ Family and marriage problems
_____ On the job
_____ "It's going to be a rough day so I'll take a couple just in case."

3. Growing rigidity in life styles.
_____ Cannot go anywhere without supply of medication
_____ Has particular times during day for participation
_____ Limits "social" activities to those, which involve their habit
_____ Self-imposed rules beginning to change, Saturday lunch etc.
_____ Will not tolerate interference during this time or change amounts

4.   Growing tolerance

_____   Ingenuity about obtaining the substance without other being aware
_____   Ability to hold substance without showing it, "Wooden Leg" syndrome
_____   Increase amounts or mix different chemical

5.   Lose of Control – Self
_____   Binging
_____   Continuous participation every two to three hours or twice a day
_____   Increasing blackouts
_____   Increasing blackouts and memory distortion
_____   Unplanned participation more frequent times
_____   Using another person's prescriptions
_____   repeated harmful consequences resulting from participation

6.   Loss of Control – Family
_____   Broken promises involving "cutting down"
_____   Changing family duties due to physical incapacity (Increase time in bed, lack of
motivation and drive)
_____   Participation during family rituals (Christmas, birthdays)
_____   Induced mood changes creates uncertainty and suspicion in family
        members
_____   Sacrificing other family financial needs

7.   Legal Problems
_____   Causes disorderly conduct
_____   Causes traffic violations
_____   Suits, result of impaired judgment
_____   Divorce proceedings
_____   Buys from illegal sources

8.   Social Problems
_____   Loss of friendships because of antisocial behavior
_____   Previous hobbies, interests and community activities neglected

9. Occupational Problems
_____ Absenteeism
_____ Demotions due to impaired and inappropriate behavior or poor
        performance
_____ Threats of termination
_____ Loss of Job

10. Physical Problems
_____ Numerous hospitalizations
_____ Increasing number of physical complaints
_____ Medical advice to cut down
_____ Using as medication to get to sleep or relieve stress
_____ Physical deterioration due to participation

11. The Problem of Growing Defensive
_____ Vague and evasive answers
_____ Inappropriate reactions to consequences of participation
_____ frequent attempt at switching to other areas of concern

Directions: True or False concerning a Counselor?

1. A Counselor should be direct at all times. _____
2. A Counselor should be direct but not District Attorney. _____
3. A Counselor should be persistent at all time. _____
4. A Counselor should be persistent and firm. _____
5. A Counselor should be persistent but not threatening. _____
6. A Counselor should be ready to seek out corroborating data from
7. A Concerned person, if person becomes highly defensive. _____

COCAINE WITHDRAWAL SEVERITY ASSESSMENT

Date: _____   Date of Last Cocaine Use: _____   Score

1.   OVEREATING: 0 = normal appetite; 3-4 = eats a lot more
Than usual; 7 = eats more than twice amount of food   _____

2.   UNDER EATING: 0 = normal appetite; 3-4 = eats less than
Half of normal amount; 7= no appetite at all   _____

3.   CARBOHYDRATE CRAVING: 0 = no desire; 3-4 = strong
Craving for sweets, half the time; 7 = strong craving for
Sweets, all the time   _____

4.   COCAINE CRAVING INTENSITY: 0 = no craving; 3-4 = strong
Craving for cocaine, half the time; 7 = strong craving for cocaine, all the time

_____

5.   CARVING FREQUENCY: 0 = no craving; 3-4 = strong craving
For cocaine, half the time; 7 = strong craving for cocaine, all the time   _____

6.   SLEEP I: 0 = normal amount of sleep; 3-4 = half of normal
Amount; 7 = no sleep at all   _____

7.   SLEEP ii: 0 = normal amount of sleep; 3-4 = could or do sleep
Half the day; 7 = sleep or could sleep all the time   _____

8.   ANXIETY: 0 = usually do not feel anxious; 3-4 = feel anxious
Half the time; 7 = feel anxious all the time   _____

9.   ENERGY LEVEL: 0 = feel alert and have usual amount of

Energy; 3-4 = feel tired half the time; 7 = feel tired all the time _____

10.   ACTIVITY LEVEL: 0 = no change in usual activities; 3-4 = Participate in half of usual activities; 7 = no participation In usual activities _____

11.   TENSION: 0-1 = rarely feel tense; 3-4 = feel tense half the Time; 7 = feel tense most or all the time _____

12.   ATTENTION: 0 = able to concentrate on reading; conversation Tasks, and make plans without difficulty; 3-4 = difficulty with The preceding half the time; 7 = difficulty with the preceding all the time _____

13.   PARANOID IDEATION: 0 = no evidence of paranoid Thoughts; 3-4 = unable to trust anyone; 5 = feel people Are out to get them; 7 = feel a specific person/group Is plotting against them _____

14.   PLEASURELESSNESS: 0 = ability to enjoy self remains Unchanged; 3-4 = able to enjoy self half of the time; 7 = unable to enjoy self at all _____

15.   DEPRESSION: 0 = no feelings related to sadness or Depression; 3-4 = feel sad or depressed half the time; 7 = feel depressed all of the time _____

16.   SUICIDAL: 0 = does not think about being dead; 3-4 = feel like life is not worth living; 7 = feel like actually ending life _____

17.   IRRITABILITY: 0 = feel that most things are not irritating; 3-4 = feel that many things are irritating; 7 = feel that mostly everything is irritating and upsetting _____

TOTAL _____

Note: If after a cocaine binge, you use this chart and score above 20, and then you should seek medical help for your problem. You may want to ask your doctor for a prescription of a drug called amantadine to help you get through withdrawal. This drug does not have abuse potential and can safely be used in conjunction with outpatient treatment or counseling and self-help groups. A recent study we did found that those scoring higher than 20 had virtually no chance of treatment success without medications to help with withdrawal.

Source: Adapted from WHO, AUDIT

MEMORANDUM

TO: THE LIVING-DEAD

FROM: YOUR ADDICTION

RE: "You can't trick the 'trickster'"

Sobriety and I are enemies. I substitute your happiness for sadness. Anyone who conceives life without me is my enemy. To all who come in contact with me, death is my ultimate goal for you.

Allow me to introduce myself. I am the trickster, the disease of your addiction. I am sneaky, inexplicable, powerful and tolerant. That's Me! I have killed billions and you are no different. Ha! Ha! Keep doing what you are doing and I promise, you will become one of my statistics. Catching you with the element of surprise is what I do best. Of course, you don't believe that either but keep on playing with me and we will see who has the last laugh. I will make you curse the day you were born. I am so slick, it is easy for you to mistake me for an Angel of Light. I will never present myself as I really am, not really. I love pretending. I am so clever I will become your most experienced lover and your closest friend. I will make your family seem like your worse enemy. Don't get me wrong, I will give you comfort. When you are lonely and feel down, I will pick you up. When you have had enough of me and choose death over me, I will accommodate you because you are my play toy.

You are a cry baby, and the reason I know you are, is because I make you cry. Even better, I love to anesthetize you so you can neither laugh nor cry. I give you instant satisfaction and require of you much pain and suffering. And you think you are using? Give me a break! you are being used by Me. The more you use me the weaker you get. You are so ludicrous. You really think you have the upper hand on Me. Please! Every time you use Me, I misuse you. I make you roam the streets, eat from garbage cans, steal from your family and lie like a dog. I make you hate the sun that shines and curse the darkness. I tell you what to wear, who to sleep with, when to take a bath, and where you are going to live. I am your Addiction. I am the boss.

I am a people lover and people love me. They don't take me seriously and neither do you. But you better believe I come to kill, steal and destroy. Look, just call me Death. I am THE TRICKSTER. Make no mistake about it I am POWERFUL. But don't put all the blame on me; You chose Me. You think you are going to play me and win. Don't try it; I will destroy you. No brag just facts. When I get my grip on you I will let you go when I am ready. If you get away, I will track you down. I will get you when you are asleep or awake. There is only one thing that can Save you. But I am not going to tell you what that is. You are so smart find out for yourself. But until then you are just another member of the living-dead. You are mine.

PROTECTING ABSTINENCE

Below is a list of things to help you stay abstinent. Ask yourself these questions to remind you how important it is to stay abstinent.

- With whom should you spend more time?

- What should you do to fill your spare time?

- What hobbies or interests should you begin pursuing more?

- How will you make sure to pursue them?

- How should you let people know about your changes if they ask about them or invite you to a high-risk activity?

- How should you make it known that you're now abstaining from drugs and alcohol?

- How can you keep a positive attitude about your abstinence? What should you do to make it seem worthwhile?

- Will your pride increase as you feel you're spending more and more time not drinking or using drugs?

- Is the opinion of anyone in particular important to you?

- How will you talk to those people about your abstinence?

- How can you reward yourself for staying abstinent?

- Will spending some time thinking about your success in recovery help?

- What should you look for to recognize the benefits from staying abstinent?

Source: Adapted from You Can Free Yourself from Drugs and Alcohol

A DRAFTED PLAN OF ACTION

"Relapse-Prevention Plan"

Once you are released from detox, you are encouraged to attend a meeting or fellowship. Below is a plan to help prevent relapse. Take every thought, attitude, and behavior into consideration as you answer the following questions.

(Resource Book Page 20)

- How can you avoid getting drugs or alcohol?

- Who should you avoid calling?

- How will you avoid them?

- Where should you not go?

- What kinds of events should you avoid?

- What will you do to keep from going there?

- What should you do to avoid setting yourself up to use or to drink?

- What relapse-preventing things should you make it a point to do every day, every week, every month?

- What are the things you should avoid doing so that you won't trick yourself or someone else into getting drugs or alcohol?

- What kind of mind games that you play with yourself should you learn to recognize? How will you deal with those mind games?

- What are thoughts you should recognize that in the past have signaled an upcoming relapse?

- How should you deal with those thoughts?

- What else should you do to avoid relapse?

Source: Adapted from You Can Free Yourself from Drugs and Alcohol

BIBLIOGRAPHY

Ackerman, Robert J., Children of Alcoholics: A Guidebook for Educators, Therapists, and Parents. Holmes Beach, Florida, Learning Publications, 1978.

Alcoholics Anonymous World Service, Inc., Alcoholics Anonymous. 2001

Alcoholics Anonymous. Alcoholics Anonymous: The Story of How Many Thousands of Men and Women Have Recovered from Alcoholism. Third Edition. Alcoholics Anonymous World Services, Inc., New York, 1976.

Althauser, Doug. You Can Free Yourself from Alcohol & Drugs. New Harbinger Publications, Inc., 1998

Bien, Beverly and Bien, Thomas. Mindful Recovery. New York: John Wiley & Sons, Inc., 2002

Bitter, Nernon J. Twelve Steps For Christian Living. Pymoth, Mn: ICL Renewed Life Services, 1987

Black, Claudia, It Will Never Happen to Me. Denver, Colorado, MAC Printing and Publishing Division, 1982.

Brown, Stephanie, Treating the Alcoholic, A Developmental Model of Recovery. New York, John Wiley &n Sons, Inc., 1985. Pp. 58, 75-100.

Cleave, Stephen Van. Counseling for Substance Abuse and Addiction. Word Incorporated, 1987

Cloud, Henry, Changes That Heal, How to Understand Your Past to Ensure a Healthier Future. Published in association with Yates & Yates, LLP, Attorneys and Counselors, Suite 1000, Literary Agent, Orange, CA. 1992.

Cohen, Sidney, M.D. Inhalants and Solvents. In Youth Drug Abuse: Problems, Issues and Treatment. G.M. Beschner and A.S. Friedman, eds. Lexington Books, Lexington, Mass., 1979.

Collins, Gary R., Christian Counseling, A Comprehensive Guide. Zondervan Bible Publishers, Wheaton, Ill. 1988

Conway, Flo and Siegelman, Jim, Snapping: America's Epidemic of Sudden Personality Change. New York, J. B. Lippincott Company, 1978.

_____. The Substance Abuse Problems. The Haworth Press, New York, 1981.
Copans, Stuart A. and Rich, Phil, The Healing Journey Through Addiction. New York: John Wiley & Sons, Inc., 2000.
Dearing, Norma. The Healing Tough. Grand Rapids, Michigan: Chosen Books, 2003

Drews, Toby Rice, Getting Them Sober: A Guide for Those Who Live with an Alcoholic. Plainfield, New Jersey, Have Books, Logos International.

Dulfano, Celia, Families, Alcoholism, and Recovery: Ten Stories. Hazel Crest, Illinois, the CENAPS Corporation, 1984.

Fleeman, William. The Pathways to Peace: Anger Management Workbook. Alameda, CA: Hunter House Inc., 2003

Fields, Rick, Peggy Taylor, Rex Weyler and Rick Ingrasci. Chop Wood Carry Water: A Guide to Finding Spiritual Fulfillment in Everyday Life. Jeremy P. Tarcher, Inc., Los Angeles, 1984.

Friends In Recovery. The Twelve Steps for Christians. RPI Publishing, Inc., 1988

Friends In Recovery. The Twelve Steps A Spiritual Journey. RPI Publishing, Inc., 1994

Gorski, Terence T., The Denial Process and Human Disease. Ingalls Memorial Hospital, May, 1976. Available from the CENAPS Corporation, P.O. Box 184, Hazel Crest, Illinois, 60429.

Gorski, Terence T. and Miller, Merlene. Counseling for Relapse Prevention. Herald House-Independent Press, Independence, MO, 1982.

_____. Staying Sober – A Guide for Relapse Prevention. Herald House-Independent Press, Independence, MO, 1986.

Gravitz, Herbert L. and Bowden, Julie D., Guide to Recovery: A Book for Adult Children of Alcoholics. Holmes Beach, Florida, Learning Publications, Inc., 1985.

Grinspoon, Lester, M.D., and James B. Bakalar. Cocaine: A Drug and Its Social Evolution. Basic Books, Inc., New York, 1976.

Henslin, Earl R. The Way Out of the Wilderness. Nashville: Thomas Nelson, 1991

Kaufman, Edward and Kaufman, Pauline, Family Therapy of Drug and Alcohol Abuse. New York, 1979.

Kinney, Jean. Clinical Manual of Substance Abuse. Mosby –Year Book, Inc., 1996

Klaas, Joe. The Twelve Steps to Happiness. Hazelden Foundation, Center City, Minn., 1982.

Lewis, C. S. The Problem of Pain. New York: Macmillan, 1962

Linthicum, Robert C. Empowering The Poor. MARC, a division of World Vision International, 1991

Marlatt, G. Alan and Gordon, Judith R., Relapse Prevention – Maintenance Strategies in the Treatment of Addictive Behaviors. New York, Guilford Press, 1985.

May, Gerald G., M.D., Addiction & Grace Love and Spirituality in the Healing of Addiction, HarperCollins Publishers, 10 East 53rd Street, New York, NY 10022. 1991.

Miller, J. Keith. A Hunger For Healing. Harper San Francisco, 1991

Miller, Merlene and Gorski, Terence T., Family Recovery: Growing Beyond Addiction. Independence, Missouri, Herald House Independence Press, 1982.Independence, Missouri, Independence Press, pp. 98-101, 1980.

_____. Learning to Live Again.,

Perkins, John M. Restoring At-Risk Communities. Baker Book Publications, 1995

Quinn, Robert E. Deep Change. Jossey-Bass Publishers, 1996

Sample, Tex. Hard Living People And Mainstream Christians. Abingdon Press, 1993

RPI Publishing, Inc. The Twelve Steps: A Way Out. Curtis: WA, 1995

_____. The Twelve Steps For Christians. Curtis: WA, 1994

_____. The Twelve Steps: A Spiritual Journey. Curtis: WA. 1994

Sample, Tex, Hard Living People and Mainstream Christians. Abingdon Press 1993

Tiebout, Harry M., "Conversion As a Psychological Phenomenon." Read before the New York Psychiatric Society, April 11, 1944. New York, National Council on Alcoholism, 1944.
Twerski, Abraham. Addictive Thinking. Hazelden Foundation, 1990

Valliant, George E., The Natural History of Alcoholism – Causes, Patterns, and Paths to Recovery. Cambridge, Massachusetts, Harvard University Press, 1983, pp.31-32, 172-173.

Van Cleave, Stephen, Walter Byrd, and Kathy Revell. Counseling for Substance Abuse and Addiction. Dallas: Word Publishing, 1987

Watley, William D. You Have to Face it to Fix it. Judson Press, 1997

Wegsheider, Sharon, Another Chance – Hope and Health for the Alcoholic Family. Palo Alto, California, Science and Behavior Books, Inc., 1983.

Made in the USA
Monee, IL
31 October 2020

46456689R00037